Back to School

Book 2

Level 1
Unit 1

Columbus, OH

Program Authors

Carl Bereiter
Andy Biemiller
Joe Campione
Iva Carruthers
Doug Fuchs
Lynn Fuchs
Steve Graham
Karen Harris
Jan Hirshberg
Anne McKeough
Peter Pannell
Michael Pressley
Marsha Roit
Marlene Scardamalia
Marcy Stein
Gerald H. Treadway Jr.

Photo Credits
28 © Stone/Getty Images, Inc.; **29** © The Denver Public Library; **30** © Minnesota Historical Society; **31** © Jim Craigmyle/CORBIS; **32** © Minnesota Historical Society/CORBIS; **33** © Peter Cade/Stone/Getty Images, Inc.; **34** © Minnesota Historical Society/CORBIS; **35** © Jim Craigmyle/CORBIS; **36** © SuperStock, Inc./SuperStock; **37** © photos Alyson/Getty Images, Inc.; **38** © Royalty-Free/CORBIS; **39** © Mary Kate Denny/PhotoEdit; **40** © Granger Collection; **41** © PhotoDisc/ Getty Images, Inc.; **42** © CORBIS; **43** © Blend Images/Getty Images, Inc.; **44 (cl)** The Metropolitan Museum of Art, Gift of Alexander Smith Cochran, 1913 (13.228.7) Photograph © 1984 The Metropolitan Museum of Art, **(tr)** The Louis E. Stern Collection, Philadelphia Museum of Art, **(br)** © Kactus Foto, Santiago, Chile/SuperStock

SRAonline.com

SRA

Acknowledgments
Grateful acknowledgment is given to the following publishers and copyright owners for permissions granted to reprint selections from their publications. All possible care has been taken to trace ownership and secure permission for each selection included. In case of any errors or omissions, the Publisher will be pleased to make suitable acknowledgments in future editions.

From WOLF! by Becky Bloom, illustrated by Pascal Biet. Published by Orchard Books, an imprint of Scholastic, Inc. Copyright © 1999 by Siphano, Montpelier. Reprinted by permission of Scholastic, Inc.
SCHOOL: THEN AND NOW by Robin Nelson. Text copyright © 2003 by Lerner Publications Company. Reprinted with the permission of Lerner Publications Company, a division of Lerner Publishing Group. All rights reserved. No part of this text excerpt may be used or reproduced in any manner whatsoever without the prior written permission of Lerner Publishing Group.
"School Bus" from SCHOOL SUPPLIES. Copyright © 1996 by Lee Bennett Hopkins. Reprinted by permission of Curtis Brown, Ltd.
Reprinted with the permission of Simon & Schuster Books for Young Readers, an imprint of Simon & Schuster Children's Publishing Division from SCHOOL SUPPLIES selected by Lee Bennett Hopkins, illustrated by Renee Flowers. Illustrations copyright © 1996 Renee Flower.

An Open Court Curriculum.

Printed in Mexico.

Send all inquiries to this address:
SRA/McGraw-Hill
4400 Easton Commons
Columbus, OH 43219-6188

ISBN: 978-0-07-610924-1
MHID: 0-07-610924-0

1 2 3 4 5 6 7 8 9 RRM 13 12 11 10 09 08 07

Back to School

Book 2

Table of Contents

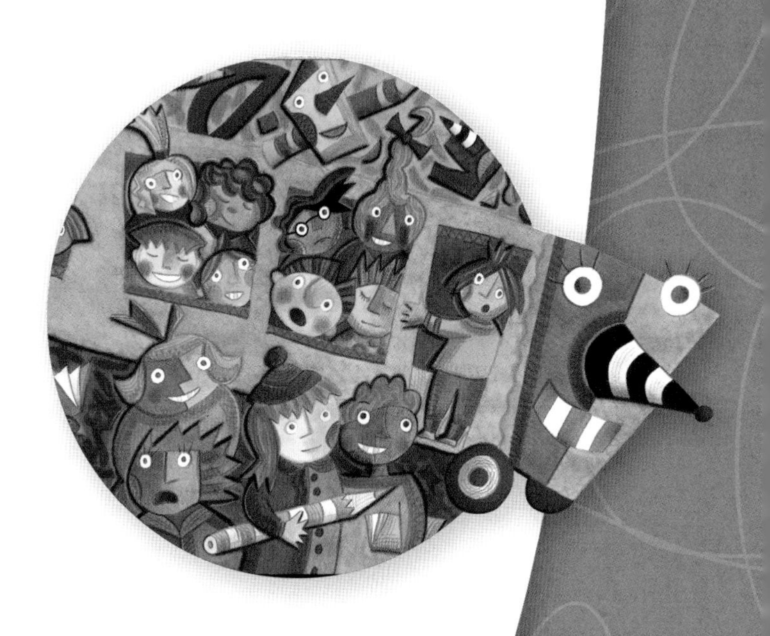

Focus Questions Have you ever worked hard to learn something new? How did it make you feel?

WOLF!

by Becky Bloom

illustrated by Pascal Biet

After walking for many days, a wolf wandered into a quiet little town. He was tired and hungry, his feet ached, and he had only a little money that he kept for emergencies.

Then he remembered. There's a farm outside this village, he thought. I'll find some food there . . . .

As he peered over the farm fence, he saw a pig, a duck, and a cow reading in the sun.

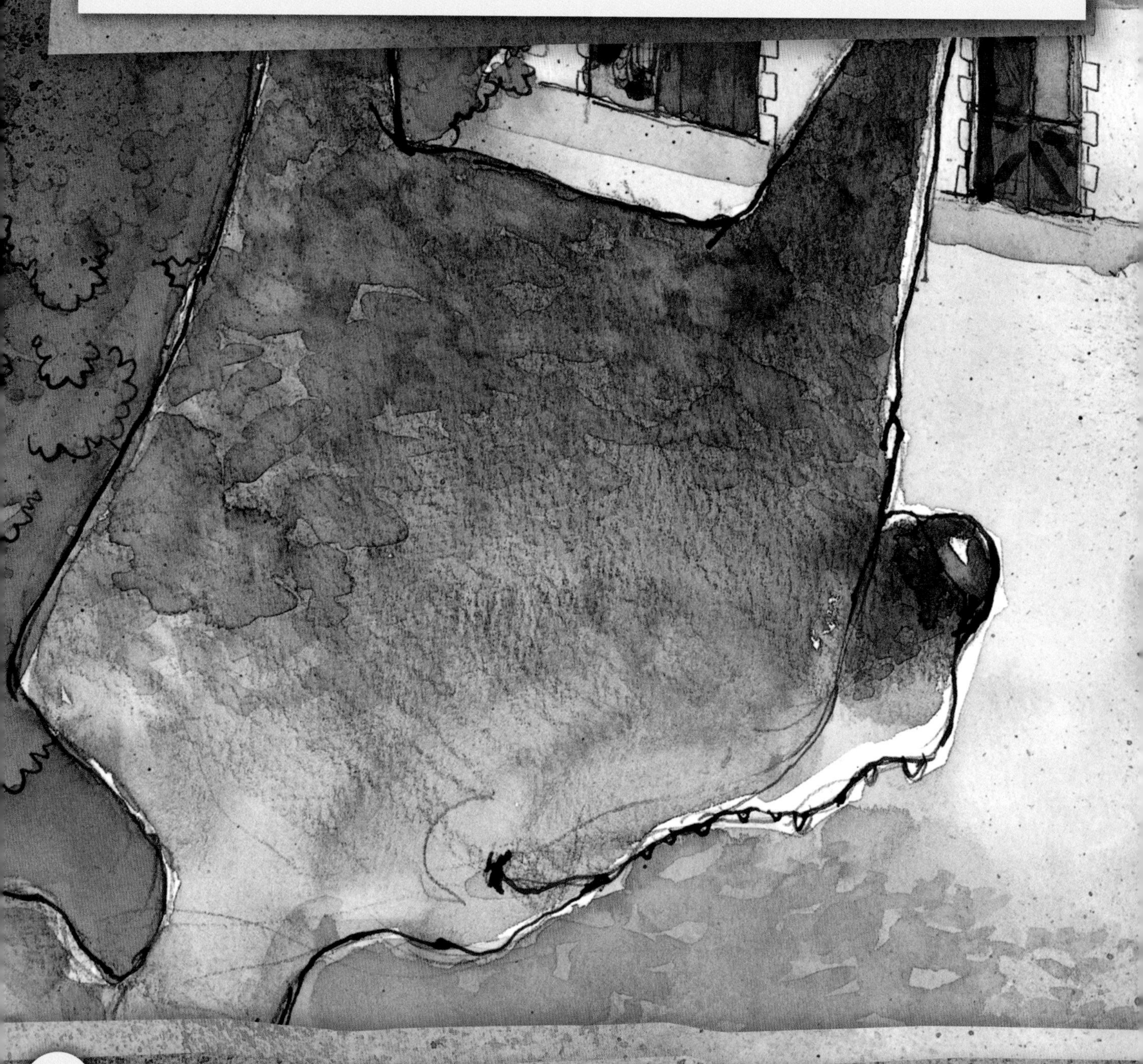

The wolf had never seen animals read before. "I'm so hungry that my eyes are playing tricks on me," he said to himself. But he really was very hungry and didn't stop to think about it for long.

The wolf stood up tall, took a deep breath . . .

. . . and leaped at the animals with a howl—
"*AaaOOOOOooo!*"

Chickens and rabbits ran for their lives, but the duck, the pig, and the cow didn't budge.

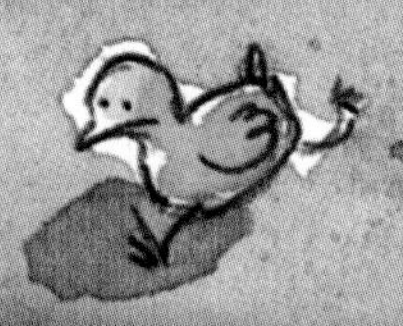

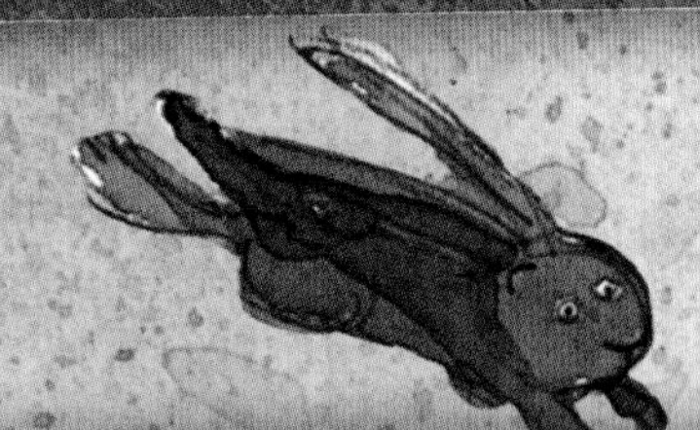

"What is that awful noise?" complained the cow. "I can't concentrate on my book."

"Just ignore it," said the duck.

The wolf did not like to be ignored.

"What's wrong with you?" growled the wolf. "Can't you see I'm a big and dangerous wolf?"

"I'm sure you are," replied the pig. "But couldn't you be big and dangerous somewhere else? We're trying to read. This is a farm for educated animals. Now be a good wolf and go away," said the pig, giving him a push.

The wolf had never been treated like this before.

"Educated animals . . . educated animals!" the wolf repeated to himself. "This is something new. Well then! I'll learn how to read too." And off he went to school.

The children found it strange to have a wolf in their class, but since he didn't try to eat anyone, they soon got used to him. The wolf was serious and hardworking, and after much effort he learned to read and write. Soon he became the best in the class.

Feeling quite satisfied, the wolf went back to the farm and jumped over the fence. I'll show them, he thought.

He opened his book and began to read: *"Run, wolf! Run! See wolf run."*

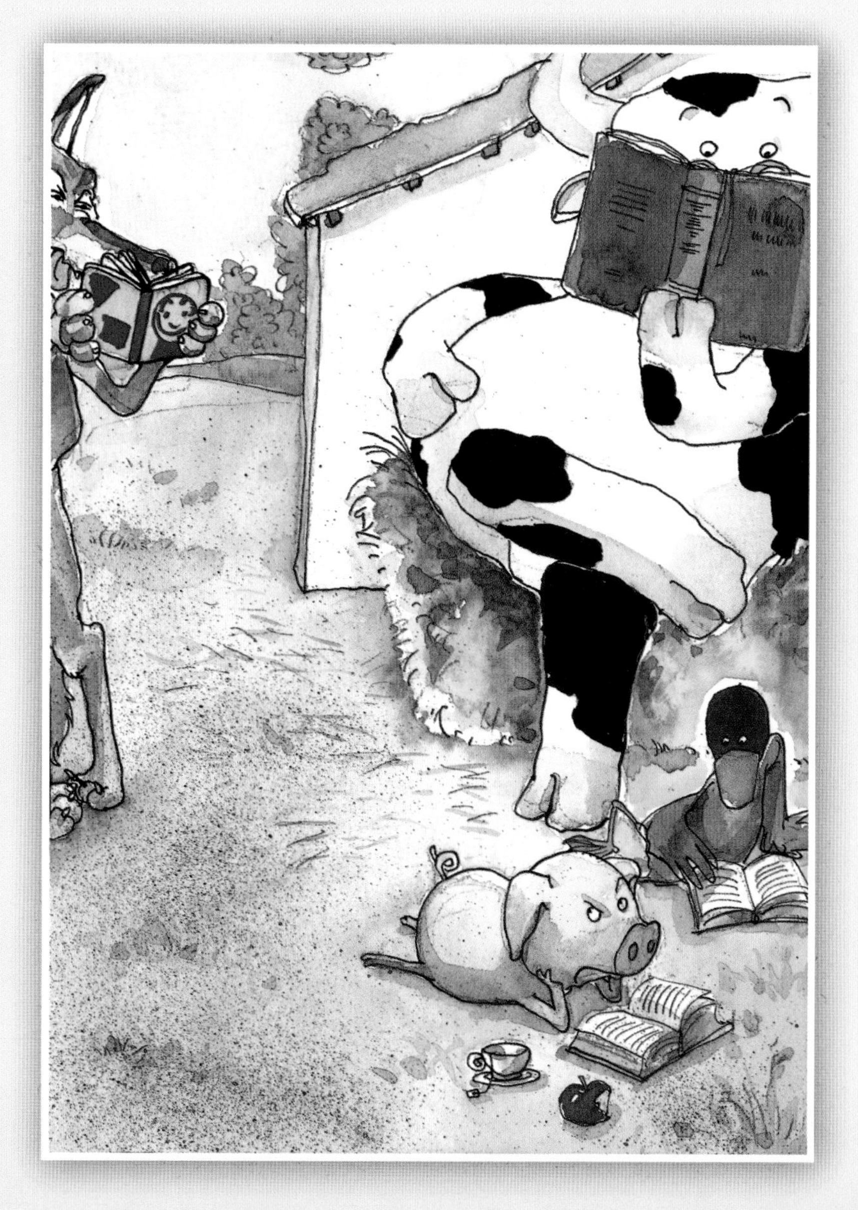

"You've got a long way to go," said the duck, without even bothering to look up. And the pig, the duck, and the cow went on reading their own books, not the least impressed.

The wolf jumped back over the fence and ran straight to the public library. He studied long and hard, reading lots of dusty old books, and he practiced and practiced until he could read without stopping.

"They'll be impressed with my reading now," he said to himself.

The wolf walked up to the farm gate and knocked.

He opened *The Three Little Pigs* and began to read:

"Onceuponatimetherewerethreelittlepigsoneday theirmothercalledthemandtoldthem—"

“Stop that racket,” interrupted the duck.

“You have improved,” remarked the pig, “but you still need to work on your style.”

The wolf tucked his tail between his legs and slunk away.

But the wolf wasn't about to give up. He counted the little money he had left, went to the bookshop, and bought a splendid new storybook. His first very own book!

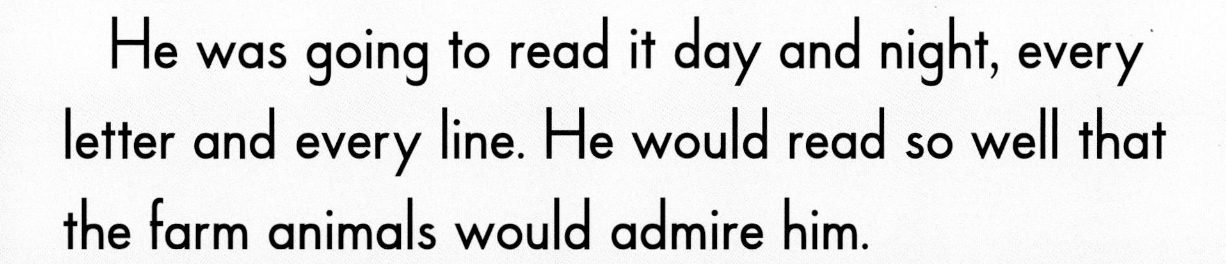

He was going to read it day and night, every letter and every line. He would read so well that the farm animals would admire him.

Ding-dong, rang the wolf at the farm gate.

He lay down on the grass, made himself comfortable, took out his new book, and began to read.

He read with confidence and passion, and the pig, the cow, and the duck all listened and said not one word.

Each time he finished a story, the pig, the duck and the cow asked if he would please read them another.

So the wolf read on, story after story. One minute he was Little Red Riding Hood, the next a genie emerging from a lamp, and then a swashbuckling pirate.

"This is so much fun!" said the duck.

"He's a master," said the pig.

"Why don't you join us on our picnic today?" offered the cow.

And so they all had a picnic—the pig, the duck, the cow, and the wolf. They lay in the tall grass and told stories all the afternoon long.

"We should all become storytellers," said the cow suddenly.

"We could travel around the world," added the duck.

"We can start tomorrow morning," said the pig.

The wolf stretched in the grass. He was happy to have such wonderful friends.

Focus Question What was school like long ago?

School Then and Now

by Robin Nelson

We go to school to learn and see friends.

School has changed over time.

Long ago, children had to walk many miles to school.

Now, children take buses to school.

Long ago, schools had only one room.

Now, schools are large buildings with many rooms.

Long ago, children in your class were many ages.

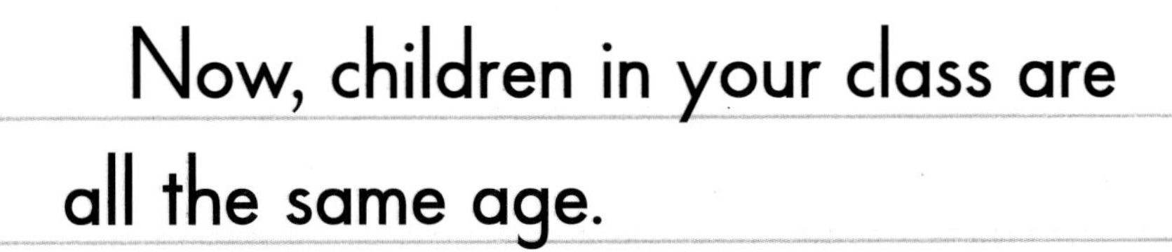

Now, children in your class are all the same age.

Long ago, students had to share a desk.

Now, students have their own desks.

Long ago, students wrote on slates.

Now, students write in notebooks.

Long ago, students wrote with chalk.

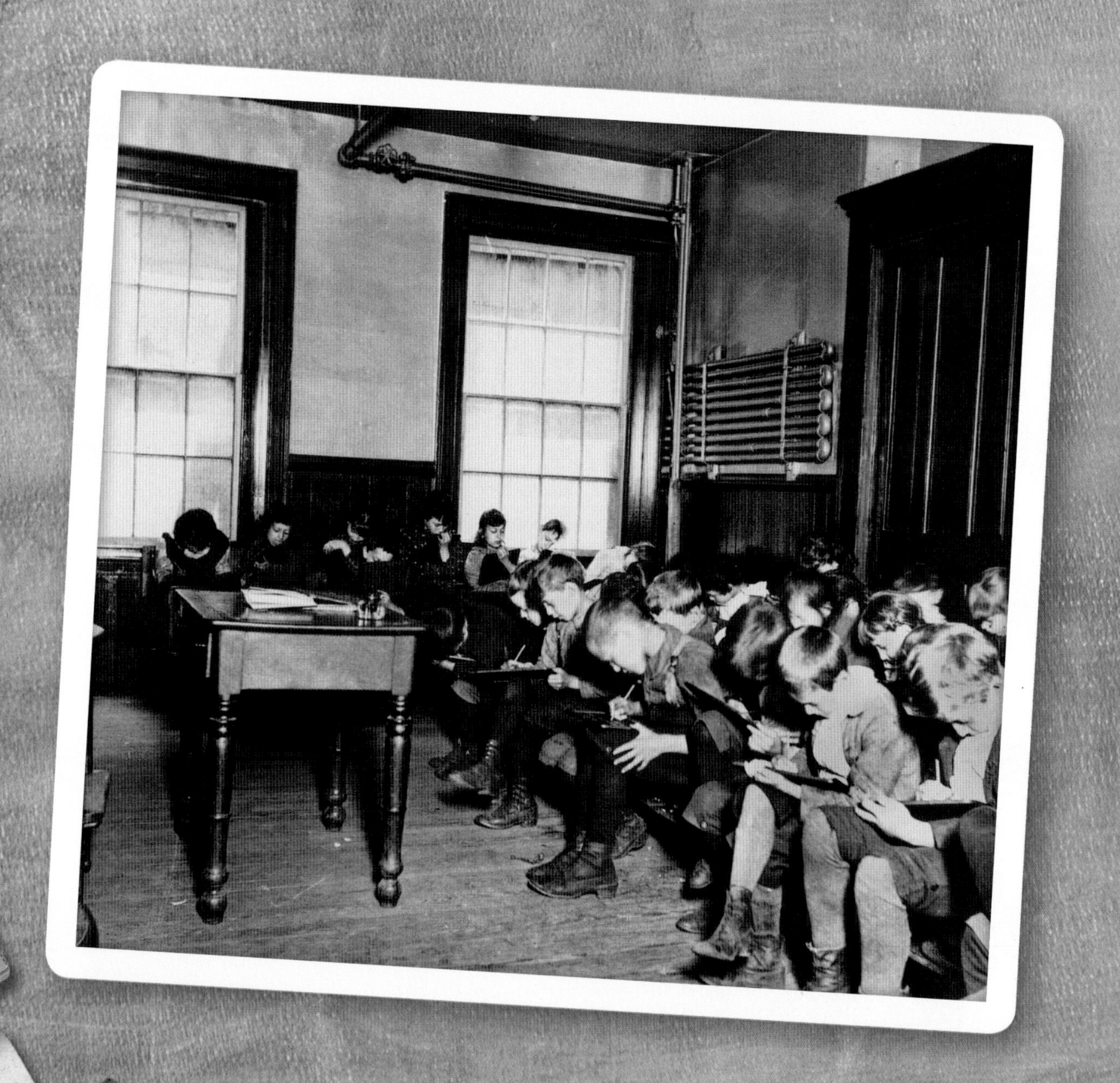

Now, students write with pencils.

Long ago, students learned reading, writing, and arithmetic.

Now, students also learn science and social studies.

Schools Time Line

1565
Pencil is invented.

1635
First public school opens.

1636
Harvard, the first college, is started.

1828
Noah Webster publishes his first dictionary.

1873
First public kindergarten opens.

1882
Fountain pen is invented.

1900
Paper clip is invented.

1658
First children's picture book is published.

1731
First public library opens.

1708
First illustrated history book is published.

1821
First public high school opens.

1903
Crayola crayon is invented.

1939
School buses are painted yellow.

1938
Ballpoint pen is invented.

1943
Computer is invented.

Focus Question

Why does the author say the school bus is wide awake?

School Bus

by Lee Bennett Hopkins

illustrated by Renée Flower

This wide-awake
freshly-painted-yellow
school bus

readied for Fall

carries us all—

Sixteen boys—
Fourteen girls—

Thirty pairs of sleepy eyes

and

hundreds
upon
hundreds

of

school supplies.

Back to School

Jacob Lawrence. *The Libraries Are Appreciated.* 1943.

Gouache and watercolor on paper. Philadelphia Museum of Art, Philadelphia, Pennsylvania.

Artist Unknown. *Layla and Majnun at School.* 1524–1525.

Style of Shaykh Zadeh. Persian (Herat) miniature; ink, colors, and gold on paper. The Metropolitan Museum of Art, New York, New York.

Arturo Gordon Vargas. *La lectura.* 1853–1933.

Chilean Kactus Foto. Santiago, Chile.

Glossary

A

ached

Joe's feet **ached** after running the race.

arithmetic

Kayla does her **arithmetic** work in math class.

B

bookshop

Chloe buys books at the **bookshop**.

C

chalk

Our teacher uses **chalk** to write on the board.

E

emergencies

Firefighters drive trucks with loud sirens to many **emergencies.**

F

fall

During the **fall,** some leaves change color and drop to the ground.

fountain pen

Dad wrote a letter with his **fountain pen.**

I

illustrated

This book is **illustrated** with pretty pictures.

L

library
Our class visits the **library** to borrow books.

M

money
Kevin uses **money** to buy his lunch.

P

picnic

We ate sandwiches and juice outside at a **picnic.**

published

The book Kate wrote was **published** and sold at the bookstore.

S

school

Logan rides to **school** on a bus.

science
We learn about plants and animals in our **science** class.

slates
In the past, children wrote on **slates** instead of paper.

supplies
You need many **supplies** when you go to school.

V

village

A **village** is a small town where people live and work.

W

wolf

A **wolf** has pointed ears, sharp teeth, and a bushy tail.